THE

FONT-DE-GAUME

CAVE

Cave painting,
protection,
conservation, interventions.

PIERRE FANLAC ÉDITEUR

PÉRIGUEUX

Representations in the terminal diverticulum *(description page 22)*.

AUTHORS :

Paulette DAUBISSE
Responsable de la Grotte Font-de-Gaume, Ministère de la Culture

Pierre VIDAL
Ingénieur au Laboratoire de Recherche des Monuments Historiques

Jean VOUVÉ
Maître-Assistant. Centre d'Hydrogéologie. Université de Bordeaux I

Jacques BRUNET
Ingénieur au Laboratoire de Recherche des Monuments Historiques

Translated by Alain SPIQUEL

I N 1902, *one of the first scientific publications concerning the Font-de-Gaume cave and the colours used by prehistorical artists came out at the Anthropological Society. The cave itself had been discovered a year before.*

In 1984, we prepared and published this popular work.

Between these extreme dates, we must mention the year 1968, when the first didactic and specific work about the cave paintings at Font-de-Gaume was printed : it was entitled « Font-de-Gaume in Perigord » and had been prepared by curator SARRADET.

This beautiful cave was not dealt with in publications as varied and rich as that of Lascaux ; yet, it is quite fascinating with all the wonders it conceals and the beauty of its site.

Have tourists ever been mistaken about it ? Have they ever been reluctant to climb the four hundred yards of steep slopes which lead them from the bottom of the small verdant vale to a kind of rocky double-pavilioned auditorium ? As soon as he has reached this natural antechamber, the visitor is entranced at the sight of the powerful overlooking cliff with its alternately hollowed out and bulging flanks, worn by water and time.

What a sight again when, the day drawing to its close, the tourist, with his head teeming with animal scenes and with the reds, browns and blacks which adorn them, perceives, on his way back, the dazzling lights of the setting sun lingering now on a corbelling, now on some of the tiny apertures opening in the high walls and from which, as Chateaubriand put it for other places, some black and glossy-winged rooks sometimes happen to shoot, glazed with red by the last gleams of daylight.

The rays which fall directly upon the scene, associated with those filtered through the foliage, seem to animate the powerful rock work, alternately yellowed with oxydation and blackened by stripes of manganese and colonies of lichens.

It is the selfsame movement, revealed some 15 000 years ago by the Magdalenians that we shall endeavour to revive through the text and illustrations of the first part of this book.

Then we shall evoke the researches devoted to the cave and the plateau as well as the direct interventions on the walls, in order to explain to whoever may be interested in this monument, a witness of a past time which is an honour to us, how it has been preserved.

J. VOUVÉ.

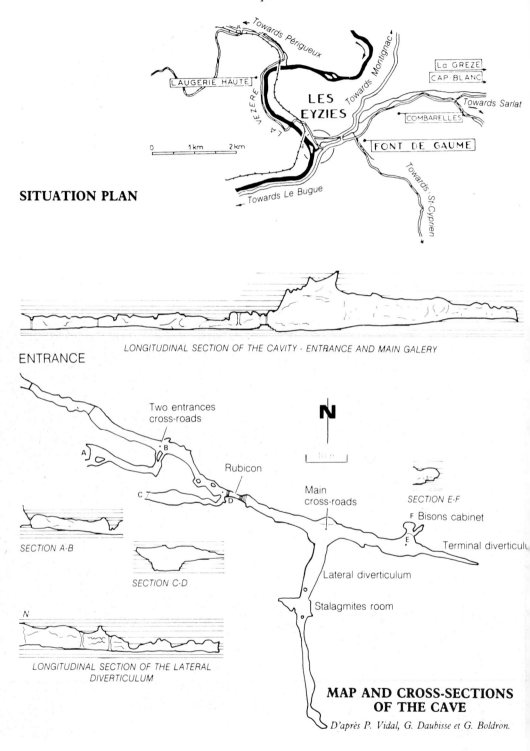

SITUATION PLAN

0   1km   2km

Towards Périgueux

LAUGERIE HAUTE

LA VEZERE

LES EYZIES

Towards Montignac

La GREZE

CAP·BLANC

Towards Sarlat

COMBARELLES

FONT DE GAUME

Towards St-Cyprien

Towards Le Bugue

LONGITUDINAL SECTION OF THE CAVITY - ENTRANCE AND MAIN GALERY

ENTRANCE

Two entrances
cross-roads

N

A   B

Rubicon

C

D

Main
cross-roads

SECTION E-F

F Bisons cabinet

E

Terminal diverticul

SECTION A-B

Lateral diverticulum

SECTION C-D

Stalagmites room

N

*LONGITUDINAL SECTION OF THE LATERAL
DIVERTICULUM*

**MAP AND CROSS-SECTIONS
OF THE CAVE**

D'après P. Vidal, G. Daubisse et G. Boldron.

Cave entrance. A group of scholars and visitors at the beginning of the century.

Prehistorical context

BEFORE examining the drawings in the cave, it may be necessary to go a few scores of years back in order to reconstitute or imagine what the discovery of the paintings at Font-de-Gaume, on September 12th, 1901, could mean. Even though the hollow was discovered on that day by Denis PEYRONY, a schoolmaster in Les Eyzies, it was not totally unknown to the public. Font-de-Gaume was easy of access, half way up a calcareous cliff facing west : it must have been a tempting goal for walks and a sort of playground for children. Let us listen to Denis PEYRONY relating his discovery to Henri BREUIL : *Today, in another cave, I have just discovered some magnificent paintings, but unfortunately a little degraded by the inscriptions visitors have left on them. There are some engravings too, but they are not so deep as those in Combarelles.*

It was frequented in the nineteenth century. The number of visitors is difficult to assess; at that period, nothing or next to nothing was known about prehistory. However some hoards, remains of ancient dwellings and occupied sites were known to a few scholars.

Cave painting was not known, in spite of the numerous artifacts and decorated bones found with the remains of flint tools in the archeological levels excavated. The first decade of the twentieth century will stick in men's memory as the moment when the paleolithic cave paintings discovered at the end of the previous century were first acknowledged from a scientifc point of view. In 1878, the discovery of the engravings in the Chabot cave, at Aigueze (Gard) by a schoolmaster passed unnoticed : in 1879, Marcelino de SAUTUO-LA, excavating at the Altamira cave, revealed the magnificent ornamented ceiling. After many a harsh and sarcastic remark, this discovery falls into oblivion too. Still later, the discovery of the Figuier cave (Ardèche) in 1880 and of the Pair-non-pair cave at Marcamps (Gironde) in 1883 (the engravings were published in 1893) constitute as many landmarks which likewise escaped notice.

Not until the discovery of La Mouthe (Les Eyzies-de-Tayac) and the publication by Émile RIVIÈRE could François DALEAU, the discoverer of Pair-non-Pair, address himself to the recording and first interpretation of the engravings on the walls. On November 13th, 1896 he could then fully describe a dozen animal representations for the Archeological Society in Bordeaux.

In 1987 the discovery of the paintings in the Marsoulas cave did not prove more convincing. All these facts give a general insight into the state of mind ot the people at the end of the nineteenth century; at the beginning of the twentieth century men such as Denis PEY-RONY started exploring the cavities they knew. The Combarelles cave (Les Eyzies) was discovered a few days before Font-de-Gaume (September 8th, 1901). The entrance of the first cavity, a vast porch, was used by the owner to shelter his cattle.

By the way, let us notice how uninterruptedly these sites have been occupied through the millenaries : the very entrance of the Combarelles cave which had protected the Magdalenian people from inclement weather was tardily turned into a shelter for domestic animals.

Reception of visitors and beginning of the path leading to the cave, under the rocky spur of Font-de-Gaume.

Besides, the owner's dwelling house is contiguous to the porch and was built against the cliff. So, on September 8th, by the light of a mere candle, after a hundred yards' trudging along, Doctor CAPITAN, Denis PEYRONY, Mr. POMAREL, the owner and Henri BREUIL saw the first animals of a living book of beasts which was to reveal more than 291 engravings (according to Henri BREUIL's inventory) : we could add *a hundred fragments of pictures too bad or in too bad a condition to allow identification* (BREUIL 1952). Among the main figures we can distinquish 116 Equidae, 37 bisons, 19 bears, 14 reindeer, 13 mammoths, 9 ibexes, 7 Bovidae, 5 stags, 5 lions, 3 hinds, 1 fallow-deer, 4 wolves (but three are doubtful), 1 fox, 1 rhinoceros, 1 fish (?), 1 snake (?). Besides there is a hand externally fringed with black, 4 tectiforms, 39 human or anthropomorphic figurations, 4 sexual signs. This long-established inventory can now be completed with the outcome of new researches led by Claude BARRIERE and Monique ARCHAMBEAU.

On the 12th of September 1901, Denis PEYRONY came to Font-de-Gaume, secretly hoping to find there what he had seen a few days before in the Combarelles cave. He was still bearing in mind the wonderful whole of the Combarelles : this was to be the beginning of a magnificent adventure, the first discovery of polychrome cave paintings in Perigord. BREUIL and CAPITAN's studies and surveys have revealed more than 180 figures : they are still reference works and we must quote Henri BREUIL's very words : *Taken as a whole, the set of representations in Font-de-Gaume is composed of 80 bisons, 40 horses, 23 mammoths, 17 reindeer and Cervidae, 8 primitive oxen, 4 Capridae, 2 rhinoceros, 1 or 2 felines, 1 wolf, 1 bear, 1 man, to which we should add 4 human hands, 19 tectiforms, 5 or 6 varied signs, that is to say 198 defined or more or less identifiable figures, plus a number of unidentified remains.* The authenticity of these painted or engraved figures was demonstrated by Henri BREUIL, doctor CAPITAN and Denis PEYRONY : they thus ackowledged cave painting as an art, a witness of the creative spirit and genius of those men of the Stone age (upper paleolithic). At the present time, 230 figures have been recorded, and thanks to the modern means of investigation, we can be sure there are many more hidden behind the abundant concretions on the walls.

The cave were privileged places during the prehistoric ages ; so we shall try and find out what the motivations of our Magdalenian ancestors were, as far as caves are concerned. In order to remove all uncertainty, we can assert the caves, no doubt, had a deep meaning ; religious, for sure, but anyway, they were certainly not places where men lived the whole year round.

One of the characteristic features of the art we are going to discover is the repetition of figures, maybe artificially assembled into wholes ; through these few delineations, we shall try and imagine those remote civilizations and work out a modern picture of them, as different as possible from the obsolete and caricatural ones provided by

Main gallery. A black bison with red horns, at the bottom of the right wall, just before the cross-roads with the lateral gallery.

a hackneyed folklore. Nowadays, we know they were not more primitive than we can be and what happens everyday in the world suffices to prove it. Thanks to those Magdalenian paintings, we are invited to sail upstream towards our origins and understand what these artists have been able to conceive at Font-de-Gaume.

On the whole, the figures recognized by Henri BREUIL are still quite legible, and in spite of seventy odd of years' visits, most of the paintings he described are irrefutable.

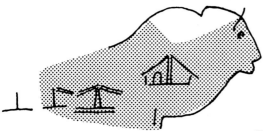

Exploring the cave

The Font-de-Gaume cave opens about twenty yards above the bottom of a small valley. Sheltered by a rocky overhang, a small natural level stretch gives access to a first cavity, a few yards deep, and to a gallery which prolongs the prehistoric cave explored. The latter is 130 yards long, and an average of 2 or 3 yards wide ; it may occasionally be more than 30 feet deep. It consists of a main gallery, on which there are, grafted, a first bent diverticulum opening directly on to the outside, a smaller gallery and then, after a narrow channel (the Rubicon) a lateral diverticulum, and a small half-domed room, the Bisons Cabinet.

The main gallery has been carved by underground waters on both sides of a subvertical cleavage plane ; the secondary channel has developped along a fracture plane perpendicular to the first. The formation of the cavity has thus been conditioned by the structural accidents affecting the calcareous plateau.

The first works still visible can only be found some fifteen yards away from the entrance : this can be explained by the hostile conditions which prevailed in the parts close to the entrance : they were the most exposed to external climatic changes and to degradation. After a careful examination of the walls covered with concretions in this first portion, Mrs. DAUBISSE could discover a number of original prehistoric sketches.

The decorated portion usually shown to visitors begins after the Rubicon, the narrow passage which has reduced the air-exchanges between the deeper part and the entrance of the cave.

Main gallery, left wall. Reindeer and bisons at the cross-roads on the upper part of the wall. Notice the important calcitic film.

Main gallery. Among the numerous figures recorded at Font-de-Gaume, we shall choose a small sample, those usually described during the visits — the exhaustive description of all the prehistoric outlines lying outside the scope of this work. After the Rubicon, the Magdalenians drew a whole sequence of polychrome animals which can be subdivided into a series of bisons whose outlines are vigorously accentuated by marks of scraping, finely engraved mammoths and little black-brown horses. The whole betrays a great concern for composition; we must admire our ancestors' acute sense of observation, their great skilfulness, their perfect mastery of the support. The outlines of these paintings are in general very firmly drawn, without the slightest hint of second-thought; the curves of the walls, the alternance of convexities and concavities are fully exploited. The treatment of forms, their almost sensual use, the colouring matters employed, the shading of the heavier parts of the animals bring out the scene in a staggering relief and conveys a feeling of vital strength.

The anatomy of the animals seems perfect in spite of the distortions characteristic of the style and of the impressive disproportion, whenever the support permits it. In this series, which occupies the first part of the main gallery, not all the figures are in a good state of preservation. Turning to the left wall, we comme across one of the most characteristic representation of Font-de-Gaume : a brown red bison whose back, hind legs, tail and belly show clear and deep marks of scraping. By contrast the details of its head are delicately carved. Superimposed to this polychrome animal, a tall mammoth can be seen : in his faultless description, Henri BREUIL singles out *the carved eye, with its clearly marked pupil. The upper outlines are amply scraped and the hind legs finely carved.*

Another series of polychrome bisons, both painted and engraved, decorates the right wall of the gallery. The tallest animal, unfortunately disfigured by graffiti made during the previous century, is a magnificent instance of animal representation in cave painting. The reliefs on the wall have been cleverly used and give the impression of a tall adult male, reinforced by the accentuation of the hump and chine;

Main gallery. Beginning of the great bison frieze on the right wall. Engraved and painted (red and black), they have been set on an outstanding relief in order to give the animals a more lively aspect.

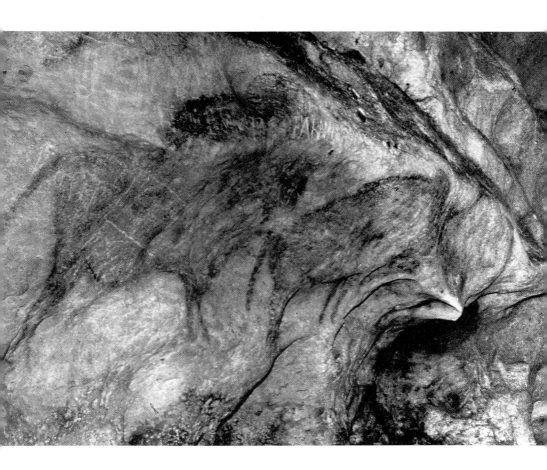

two animals follow, facing each other, both stocky, firmly planted on their legs; further on, we can see three other red bisons, with their outlines fringed with black.

These friezes always consist of males and females : it is easy to distinguish them on the painting and, no doubt it was done on purpose. Another point can be made : when we presume they are females — since there is no apparent sex organ — they seem, in the Font-de-Gaume sanctuary, to be associated to red. The colouring matters used are pigments naturally occurring anywhere in the area, mixed or not. They may have been either dabbed or blown; these techniques applied on a somewhat skew surface show the pictural mastery of the artists.

We must also try and imagine what the lighting of our ancestors was; totally different from ours, which is unfortunately too static not to fix the paintings in position.

If lit with resin torches or grease lamps, the walls as well as the pigments would be restored to life with the play of lights and shadows.

In prehistoric caves, there are not only animal representations and we should mention a whole group of signs which we are unable to undestand. They must be important since they can be found in a great many cavities, and under various forms. In certain areas, caves reveal signs which cannot be found anywhere else : tectiforms, for example. Prominent experts in cave painting, among whom A. LEROI-GOURHAN, have observed that these signs are often associated to certain animal representations : bisons, horses and mammoths are occasionally associated to this type of symbol whereas other species are not. But the mystery has never been fathomed. In Font-de-Gaume, we may discern two kinds of tectiforms, some engraved, others painted. They are usually cone-shaped and consist of a central pillar from the top of which the two sides slope downwards, the floor being symbolized by a horizontal line. From such a noun, it is tempting to derive the assumption that this sign is connected to the erection of dwellings.

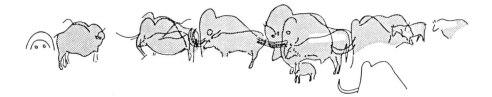

Main gallery, left wall. An engraved and scraped mammoth superimposed on a bison whose anatomical details are particularly striking.

Confronting reindeer. We are thus led to a well-known scene, probably the very symbol of Font-de-Gaume; it shows two wonderful reindeer, certainly among the most outstanding cave representations of this animal. Their attitude, the size of their horns, suggest a male and a female. The former, with its huge brown antlers, is smelling the head of the latter, which is kneeling in front of it, with its small red horns — which is already an interpretation. The two figures are unfortunately washed out, a result of the slow ageing and degradation throughout the millenaries. Let us quote Henri BREUIL's description : *The outline of the chine is deeply cut, that of the buttocks is carved and scored, the hind legs finely carved... the fore legs show a scraped and cut outline, all the details of the head and horns being quite deeply carved.*

The female, facing the male, is remarkably drawn, with precise anatomic details; her head is superbly carved under the muzzle of the male. The fore antler is distincly palmated and very finely carved. The whole line is strongly scraped, the belly is scored; on the contrary, the fore legs, bent under the animal, are not easily discernable.

This famous scene would actually refer to two animals confronting each other during a sexual parade rather than during a fight.

The reindeer and bisons at the cross-roads. On the left again, higher on the wall, we can admire a black monochrome frieze; it is a beautiful one, quite lively and very different from the others because of its reindeer and bisons shown in file. Originally, it must have been much longer and we know the rest of the painting has been covered by those calcite deposits which can be found everywhere in the caves. Those deposits may date several millenaries back and prevent us from admiring the paintings behind; but on the other hand, they prove an excellent protective layer.

We can see the body of a reindeer — remarkably done — and in full motion, a horse carved above the hindquarters, followed by a bison drawn in a thick line whose blackened head and forepart intensify the impression of power. Superimposed on it, there is a reindeer whose antlers are seen full face but whose head is unfortunately hidden with calcite. The head and part of the dorsal line of a bison follow; this "almost naïve" representation is very interesting in its simplicity, but is made still more impressive by the way the horns have been drawn. The artists have chosen to show them sideways turned on an animal drawn in profile, — the "twisted perspective" — which throws the head in stronger relief : today, we can imagine it means a backward movement. The scene has been painted on a particular spot : the only one in the cave which allows the visitor a ten yards' distance.

Main gallery. On the left, just before the cross-roads, the famous sexual parade of the reindeer.

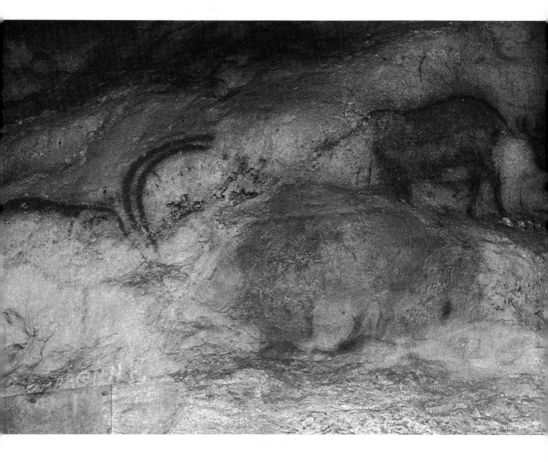

As for the first reindeer we have mentioned, it has no head : if we dismiss the hypothesis of deterioriation (the climatological as well as the microtopographical studies confirm this view) we may imagine the artist has not felt he had to draw it or been attracted to doing so. Actually, the animal is about to pass round the rocky angle which bounds the scene so the head is of little consequence for the balance of the scene as a whole.

The reindeer frieze. At the angle of the main and lateral galleries, above the ledge, the frieze is covered with a layer of calcite which obscures the outlines. Along with the two confronting reindeer, it is one of the very rare sets of reindeer known to us in the caves. The calcite veil conceals the paintings, but ensures here again a very effective natural protection.

On the right, a tall reindeer facing left and painted black comes into notice with its palmated attire ; its antlers and dorsal line are quite visible, its belly and legs vanishing under the calcite. It is superimposed on the fine outlines of two horses in file. Further to the left, we come across another reindeer with a complete body characterised by the ample palms of its attire ; a closer study reveals *a faint line carved around the muzzle and shoulder... as well as traces of scraping towards the loins, tail and legs* according to Henri BREUIL. Its hind part is partially superimposed on black lines.

Geometrical red X-shaped signs are also to be mentioned.

Angle of main and lateral galleries. Frieze of reindeer under a thick veil of calcite. The high location on the wall accounts for the intense physico-chemical activity (permanent warm air).

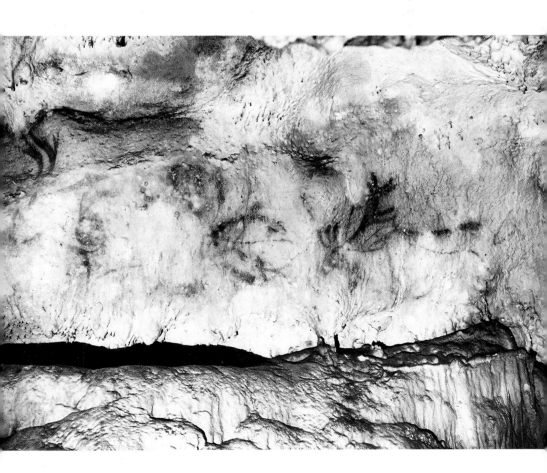

The lateral gallery. In the lateral gallery, the works are less numerous; on the right, close to the ground, we can see a polychrome bison whose fore part is very clear with its vivid red colours; it is surmounted with another bison whose outlines are hardly visible.

We can then perceive a series of three horses painted black; for at least one of them, we must insist upon the use the Magdalenian artists made of the accidents of a naturally rocky relief. The hind leg, thigh, and tail are suggested by concretions, the belly by the curve of a stalagmitic drapery. On this natural relief, they had but to underline the contours of the horse with thick black lines, which have themselves been caught in the concretionary process which has not ceased since then. No trace of retouch on these stalagmitic outgrowths which reveal, in the artists of the period, a thorough knowledge of the support and a keen sense of observation, qualities which we have already found in the artists of Lascaux. Let us then ponder over the talent, mastery and deep knowledge of the artists who were responsible for the decoration of these places.

On the other wall, not much above the level of the ground, a polychrome bison's head is covered by concretions. This gallery ends with a small room rich in stalagmites. Yet, a very narrow passage, where visitors are not allowed, permits to go on along the gallery covered with concretions up to a heap of debris not far from the outside. It shows some legible figures : a small black reindeer, a black Bovidae, a red bear and miscellaneous signs.

The last bison frieze. Let us resume our exploration in the main gallery : we are almost at the end of the visitable part; the ground has been lowered about a yard deep to put a splendid bisons frieze out of reach (on the left side). It is unquestionably the most beautiful site in Font-de-Gaume and its state of preservation is much better than that of the former paintings, unfortunately disfigured by graffiti. It must be ascribed to the layer of calcite mixted with muddy deposits which have made these paintings scarcely visible.

Five bisons, with finely engraved outlines and their bodies painted black-brown and red, loom from the background of yellow limestone and white concretions above a ledge (at least for four of them), a very lively composition. It consists of males and females; the male sexual organs are visible.

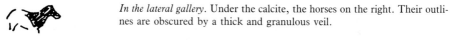

In the lateral gallery. Under the calcite, the horses on the right. Their outlines are obscured by a thick and granulous veil.

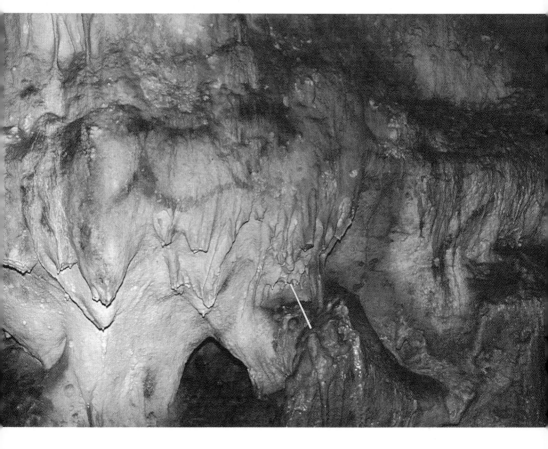

The Bison Cabinet. On the left, a little further along the main gallery, a small room has been called *the Bison Cabinet* by Messrs. PEYRONY, BREUIL and CAPITAN. Apsidiole-shaped, with a remarkable vault, it is ornated with about ten bison. Four of them are in a perfect state of preservation, among which the black bison (on the left), another one, not far away, is facing the opposite direction. Especially conspicuous is the concatenation of the tail of the first to the second and third animals. The fourth perfectly fits the concave rock : the negative aspect of such a structure is turned into a positive effect thanks to the use of colours. Other paintings can be seen, among which a very graceful head of Bovidae with lyre-shaped horns. It is a very moving recess, owing both to its small size and to the concentration and quality of drawings ; but it leaves a number of questions unanswered ; and all the natural shapes don't seem to have been fully exploited.

The main gallery ends with a narrow fissure which cannot be visited : it is decorated with a few figures, among which a feline, carved horses, a rhinoceros and some bovines.

The Bisons Cabinet. On the left part of the main gallery, the extraordinary composition on the vault.

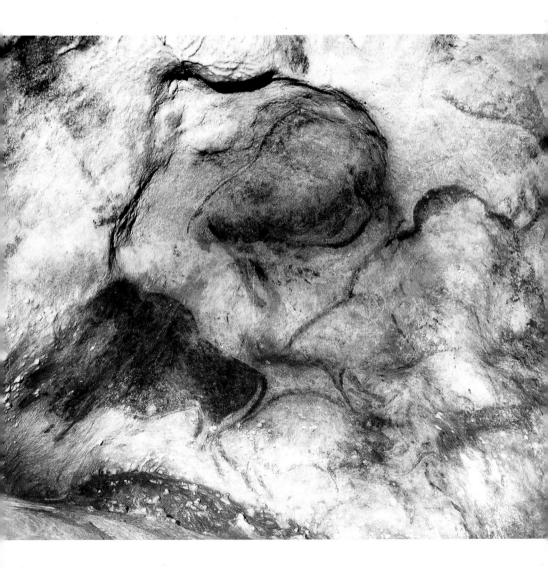

Main gallery. Frieze with five polychrome bisons half way up the left wall.

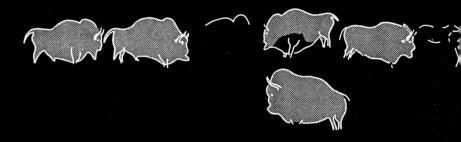

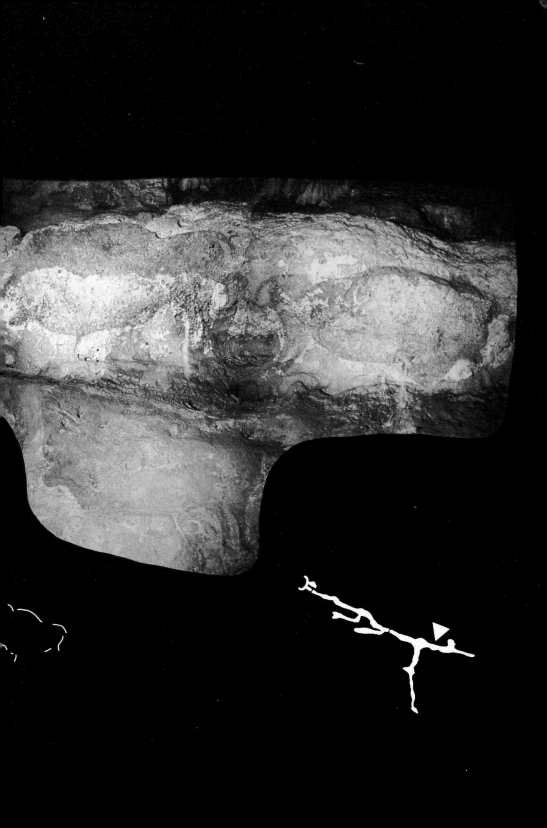

Environment and protection

Geographical,
geological and
hydrographical
setting.

As far as the natural setting of the cave is concerned, we must note it is situated at the outskirts of a vigorous calcareous massif, mostly covered with wood and with some farming areas. This massif is encircled by two main valleys towards which dry and hanging vales which open on to the top of numerous steep cliffs converge. They can be some feet to three scores of feet high.

This promontory results from the piling-up of chalky layers which date back to the Coniancian and Santonian (Cretaceous); they are covered with mixted reddish sands and clays which were transported there by powerful water flows and mud avalanches some dozen million years ago. They tumbled down the slopes of the "Massif Central" and finally flowed into the Atlantic Ocean.

Among the main stages of the process, we must remember that the sandy limestones of the Santonian have been deposited in a warm and shallow sea, limited, some twenty miles to the east, by a flat coast.

A little later, this sea moved westward and, during the Coniacian, the stratification of two distinct layers was observed.

The more recent, upper layer is made of white limestone; the older, lower one is characterised by its beige to yellow limestone mixted with a more or less important amount of sand.

This double accumulation of very compact rock has been worn out, little by little, for some ten million years, by the water of the large and small rivers, giving birth to the steep-sided cliffs and staggering overhang which overlook and surround the porch of the cave.

As for the very thickly accumulated sands and clays, they have blurred all the other reliefs of the area. Eaten away by running waters, they have been slowly worn away and carried into the sea : nowadays they only blur the top and flank of some buttes, where the beautiful chestnut forests can grow which have insured the economical balance of Perigord for centuries, producing wood and food easy to preserve during the hard and long winter months.

Aerial photograph of the site of Font-de-Gaume. Regular controls allow the plant cover to be under permanent observation. Below the arrow, the entrance of the cave can be seen.

When he enters the cave, the visitor cannot fail to be struck by certain phenomena.

First, the ornated cave is not affected by important inflows of water. In Font-de-Gaume, there is no cataract to deafen the visitors, neither winds nor fogs to lash their faces.

On the contrary, the underground atmosphere is very calm, the flowings being confined to very precise places (at the base of a calcite column, for instance), or displayed in quite thin films gleaming under the rays of the torches, along a wall or a pillar.

The water that seeps through the plateau surface and reaches the cavity much later, flowing more or less quickly along the rare vertical fractures running in the limestone, moves still slowlier through the porous rocks.

The interval between the rainy season and the moment when the water reaches the cave may last about five months for the decorated part, and from seven to ten months for the deeper portion of the network.

This hydrogeological reaction is not constant all the year through : it depends on the season, the intensity and duration of the rainfalls ; it also depends on the internal geometry of the limestones, on the breathing and perspiration of the plant cover (both activities being reduced to nothing in winter and quite intense in summer).

Compared to the other caves in Combarelles and Lascaux, Font-de-Gaume is to be classified among the "intermediary networks", that is to say among those which develop half way up the slopes. You reach Combarelles on a level ground with the bottom of the beautiful valley of the Beune, whereas you must climb up almost to the top of the hill to see the large steps leading to Lascaux.

The cave takes advantage of such a situation, which reduces the extent of the general catchment area which benefits the phreatic water in the midst of a small karstic network. Numerous valleys and secondary notches divide the subsoil into compartments, especially along the left bank of river Beune. Hence a probable cutting-up into hydrogologically independent smaller units.

Definition of the protection areas. The reader may not know that in France a law gives the state the necessary power to protect the archeological inheritance, through limitations of the right to real estate ownership (1). Such a legislative and administrative frame must be founded on field work data and documents. As far as the undergound domain is concerned, one must be aware that the protection of a cave is more complex than that of a mere classified historical monument, we must needs take into account its setting and its relations to the environment to ensure the best possible protection.

---

(1) Law passed on December 31st 1913 about classified historical monuments and allowing the protection of buildings of which the conservation is of public interest, as far as history or art is concerned. Law of the 27th September 1941 on archeological excavations, validated by ordinance on September 13th 1945.

Only a few inflows of water, on the right part, half way up the wall.

Action of insolation, precipitation, habitation and, with respect to plant cover, of the rocky mass and caving (*schematic and very general representation on a calcareous massif*).

The knowledge of the size of the cavity, its localisation in the regional geological context have allowed, after a thorough field survey, to determine three areas : their main common characteristic is the differential sensitivity to actions implying consequences on the internal conditions of the underground milieu (domestic pollution, alteration in the situation of farming and forests) according to the nature of soils, and the hydrogeological dependence (direct or belated percolation benefitting to the small aquifer drained by the ornated cave). This division into areas actually determines the surfaces under which the water-supply of the cave is more or less direct (cf. above) ; we must remind the reader of the vertical or descending subvertical character of this supply, in so far as the water inflows come partly through the vault and partly along certain portions of the walls.

These areas, characterized by their differential sensitivity, according to the stability of the environment, are defined as real protection zones of the surrounding of the Font-de-Gaume cave. We have proposed for the part we are at the moment concerned with, a sort of country planning scheme. Here is a brief description, area after area, with the list of prescriptions which it is capital to respect, in our opinion and in the present state of our knowledge.

First area, under the overhang of the cavity ; any activity must be forbidden there, the forest-clad surface must be preserved and the undergrowth maintained.

The second area corresponds to the greater part of the impluvium of the cave ; it is essential to maintain its dedication to forestry, deforestation must be strictly controlled and building forbidden.

The third area consists of the remoter parts of the impluvium ; its agro-sylvicolous vocation must be preserved and building operations regulated.

To ensure the protection of the cavity, of its surroundings, these recommendations should be strictly followed in the future in order to prevent disruptions which would prove fatal to the good state of the cavity in the short and long run.

Division into protection areas above the cave. The first area is the most sensitive : any mutation there will directly affect the cavity.

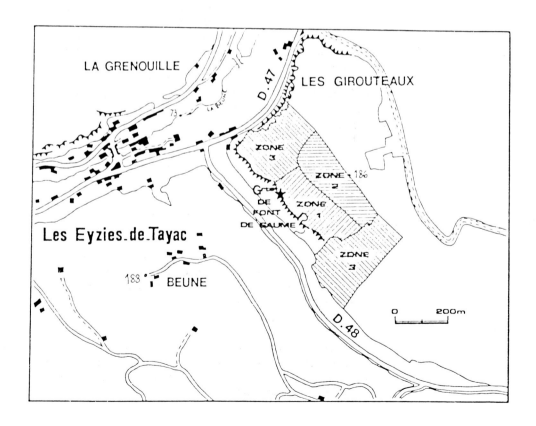

Generally speaking, the immediate surroundings of prehistorical caves are of paramount importance in their balance (preservation or degradation of cave works). The plant cover above the cavities, through the evapo-transpiration process, balances the inward percolation and largely determines the undergound climate. For instance, the climate in the Font-de-Gaume cave depends on its plant cover. The present regime of the ecocystem seems perfectly adequate to the preservation of the paintings in the cave, but the slightest alteration of the plant cover on the top of the hill or nearby would be a threat to them.

The "internal life" of the cave and its preservation.

The climate we are subjected to shows temperature changes, alterations in the direction and strength of the winds, presence or absence of rain, dry weather, clouds and so on and so forth : well, the underground realm is subjected to the same conditions, except for the rays of the sun.

Thermic study. The temperature of the air and rock are important factors of the general regime in the cave : they have been recorded thanks to precision thermometers permanently fixed in the cave and on the rock. The most representative curves of the measures, from December 1972 to November 1973, show two distinct regimes before and after the narrower part called the Rubicon : the bracket of temperatures in the first part ranging from 12 to 13 °C, that of the second part from 13 to 14° most of the time ; they also show the influence of visits from July to September when the curve of temperatures in the first part rises up to the higher bracket, while that in the second part increases correspondingly, in spite of the already limited tourist frequentation (600 people a day at the period).

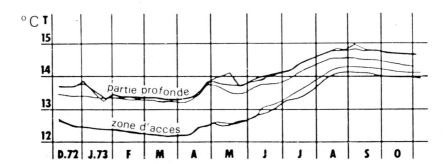

Annual variation of temperatures from December 1972 to October 1973. Two distinct regimes are clearly visible before and after the Rubicon.

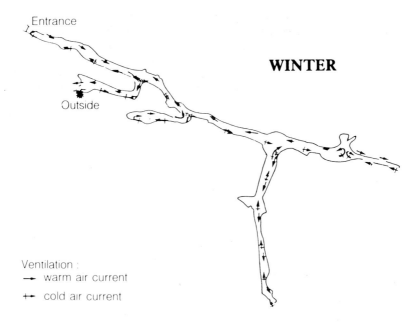

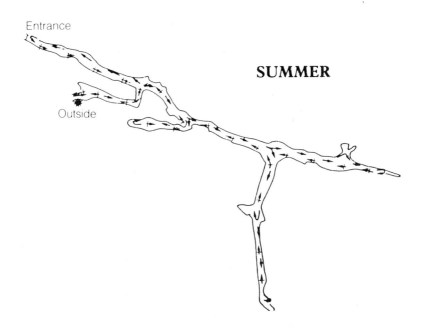

Natural ventilation of the cave in winter and summer. The diagram clearly shows how the currents flow in the opposite way according to the season.

From the numerous measures recorded from 1965 to 1980 during and outside the touristic period, with or without a limitation of the number of visitors, it is apparent that we can consider the cave as divided into two parts. The first consists of the two entrances and the access gallery until the narrow Rubicon, the second of the rest of the cavity. This natural situation is the main reason why the artistic works have been preserved; Font-de-Gaume is a cavity of the "warm air trap" kind and it is difficult for this warm air to penetrate the decorated part because of the natural obstacle of the Rubicon and of the nature of the cave which is not very much ascending. In winter, and for the selfsame reason, it is difficult for the cold air to reach the bottom, which entails a relative constancy in temperatures.

Air circulation.

On the whole, we have identified two regimes in the air circulation in Font-de-Gaume : in winter, the outer air has an influence, creating a colder current from the bent diverticulum communicating with the outside, level with the ground. Along the galleries, the warm air of the cavity is pushed upwards and circulates in the upper part. In winter, the process is reversed, the outer warmer air penetrates the upper part and drives the inner colder air to the level of the ground. Both processes are relevant when the entrance door is shut, in this case, the access gallery plays the part of a cul-de-sac for the already mentioned air circulation, and the door can play the part of a heat exchanger. These two regimes are liable to numerous variations according to the insolation of the entrances, the day and night thermic fluctuations, the atmospheric pressure and the frequentation of the cavity.

Hygrometry.

The relative humidity is at a permanently high level and close to saturation (99 %). In winter, no condensation is possible : the morphology of the cavity plays an important part : it determines the air exchanges in the cave, very locally, and is then responsible for the processes which occur where the air is in contact with the rock.

Carbon dioxide and conservation.

In principle, the rate of carbon dioxide must be as low as possible in the cavity, so as to lessen the agressiveness of condensation waters which is frequent during the touristic period. In the wet air, rich in carbon dioxide, the corrosion and therefore the assaults on the calcareous rocks can be expressed by the global chemical formula

$$CaCO_3 + CO_2 + H_2O \rightleftharpoons Ca(CO_3 H)_2$$
solid   dissolved   dissolved

According to the reaction, the adding of carbon dioxide provokes the formation of soluble bicarbonate and the absence of the gas leads to the decomposition of the bicarbonate : the limestone precipitates under the form of carbonate. In the presence of condensation water carbon dioxide is then a threat to the cave paintings : it can entail dissolution as well as, through evaporation, a limestone deposit.

In this part of the cave, temperatures and humidity are constant : hence a good state of preservation.

Control over the rate of carbon dioxide

Systematic measures recorded in the morning and in the evening at different spots of the networks, before and after visits, in 1969 and 1971, during a period when there was no limitation of the visits, have enabled us to assess the direct consequences of the visits and have revealed :

— the existence of a rate of carbon dioxide naturally ranging from 0,1 to 0,3 % ; this weak percentage corresponds with the figures recorded elsewhere in this type of subhorizontal cavity. The origin of the gas is pedological, a result of the degradation of organic matter in the superficial horizons of the ground ;

— an annual cycle and the variation of carbon dioxide all the year round ;

— a close relation between the percentage of gas and the number of visitors ;

— the part played by the Rubicon : in the decorated part, 2 % of carbon dioxide was recorded when the number of visitors rose above 800 ; we must also notice that the amount was never below 1 % during the three summer months at that period.

— the possibility (within a daily cycle) of a natural elimination thanks to the normal circulation of air and in spite of the obstacle. As a matter of fact, during the night, the air of the decorated part, which is warmer and richer in carbon dioxide, diffuses into the rest of the gallery to the entrance and the first part ; the figures recorded in the morning prove a rise in the rate of carbon dioxide compared to the day before. In some cases, behind the entrance door, the level can reach some 0,4 % corresponding to a fall of 0,3 % to 0,5 % in the decorated part.

Recommendations.

After analysis and control of several annual cycles aiming at studying the evolution of temperatures, humidity and carbon dioxide, we have been led to advise the limitation of the frequentation of the cavity. Under the previous conditions of visits (there came up to 1 500 people a day) we had noticed a very important rise for each of these interactive parameters, a rise on which we had no means of intervention. Unable to master all of them, we have imagined to choose one, since they are closely linked and determine the type of calcic evolution of the walls. With this end in view, we have chosen to control the rate of carbon dioxide.

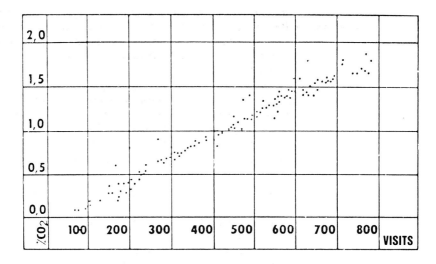

Evolution of the rate of carbon dioxide in the air main cross-roads according to daily visits.

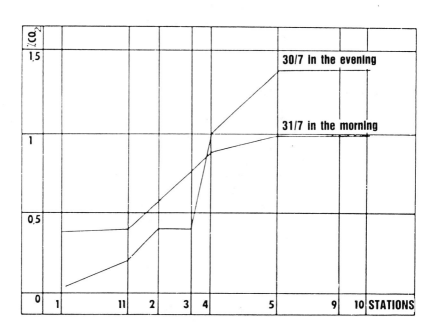

Comparison of the rate of carbon dioxide in the atmosphere of the cave between the evening and the following morning in July 1970 (stations *4, 5, 9 and 10 correspond to the decorated part*).

Principles. The cavity setting is subject to the outside influences and, at some periods of the year (in winter and spring) some of the ornated and concretion-covered parts are exposed to the streaming of infiltrated waters; at other periods (in summer), apart from the thunder rains, the influence of which is limited by the evapotranspiration, the condensation process is the only threat, because of the risk of dissolution. We are then confronted with an antinomy between the attack against the wall at a period and the risk of a concretion deposit at another. It is therefore necessary to modify the amount of carbon dioxide in the air : we must lessen its concentration very much in the first case and diminish it only very slightly in the second.

That is the reason why we eliminate the carbon dioixide in summer and limit the tourist frequentation; conversely, in winter, we let the cavity return to its millenary natural balance.

The elimination of carbon dioxide has been favoured by the digging of a slight depression which helps the air exchanges between the decorated portion and the access with its two entrances : the air deficit is compensated in a diffuse way and is progressively renewed thanks to the first part and the cracks in the rock.

The device consists of a system of pipes starting from three air aspirating vents situated on a level with the ground and leading to an eduction turbine in the bent diverticulum.

Devised for a maximum theoretical daily frequentation of 650 persons, by groups of 20, the system maintains a rate of 0,6 % of carbon dioxide in the ornated galleries thanks to the turbine : its discharge is of 264 m³ per hour.

During the pumping and to prevent any brutal relation with the outside, the additionnal doors built in the access gallery remain closed while the turbine is working during the touristic period. They are reopened when the number of visitors is smaller. At that moment, the natural ventilation is enough and the machine is stopped.

Real evolution. Numerous controls have been made after the installation of the eliminating device; as an example, we shall refer to that of August 1976 when measures were recorded hour after hour during a visit, on a day when 650 persons visited the cavity (their number being roughly the same in the morning and in the afternoon). On the next day, after the turbine had worked all night long, the rate of carbon dioxide was practically reduced to nothing (below 0,1 %) : there was no gas left from the day before.

Since 1979, the frequentation of the cavity has been reduced, not because of carbon dioxide, but owing to the problems created by the management of the groups of visitors and the strict enforcement of the preservation measures.

The system of pipes, air aspirationg vents and turbine used to eliminate the carbon dioxide.

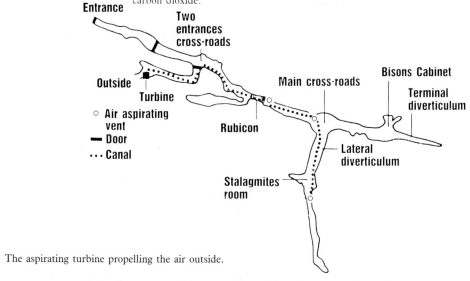

The aspirating turbine propelling the air outside.

Conservation and interventions.

The importance and archeological value of the cave paintings at Font-de-Gaume have justified and required several studies so as to harmonize the imperative conservation of the paintings and engravings with their equally necessary presentation to the general public. As soon as 1966 the delicate operation of cleaning the cavity started, under the responsibility of the "conservation des Bâtiments de France, Aquitaine" (Aquitaine French Buildings Conservancy). Since then, other interventions and researches aiming at exploring the working and the part played by the different factors of conservation have taken place.

The following intervention has been devised in order to fight the algae, particularly abundant at Font-de-Gaume : they were progressively spreading over most parts of the walls ; the blackish aspect of the gallery required a new technique of washing, so the whole cave could be cleaned.

The mechanical methods used to eliminate calcite. Three techniques have been used : shock ; brushing and wearing. The experimental area chosen was a polychrome bison on the left wall of the lateral gallery. All the methods mentioned have been tried and tested on this surface.

Most of the drawings discovered had been concealed by a layer of grey calcite which did not stick much to the base but made the paintings hardly visible and favoured the decomposition of the rock and works of art. Abundant water flows circulated between the old calcite deposits and the wall itself : it was vital to cure the decorated panels lest they should be irretrievably ruined. With the help of a small mallet made of very hard plastic, the calcite veils and flows which covered the paintings could be scaled by weak shocks. The observation of the scales through a binocular microscope has shown

In the lateral gallery. A polychrome bison at the bottom of the left wall. Experimental surface chosen for the tentative intervention.

only tiny particules of pigment on the contact surface. Besides, the lines on the rock appeared in a relief on the calcite fragments removed (for instance, a tectiform carved on the bison), but were not the least deteriorated on the original. The method, duly tested, was applied on the five bison frieze in the main gallery and permitted to set off and save this splendid painted and engraved whole which had also been covered with an argillaceous deposit making it practically invisible.

Tectiform carved on a head of bison (discovered after intervention).

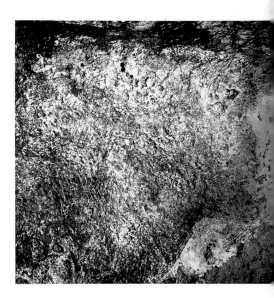

Tectiform in relief on the scale.

Contrarily to the previous phenomenon, portions of the walls were covered with a thin, very pulverulent film of calcite (5/10 mm). The dry use of a supple brush has been sufficient to eliminate the resulting opacity and to discover the painted lines. The Bisons Cabinet has been treated likewise; this method has also proved useful for the greater part of the figures at Font-de-Gaume. For the areas covered with a thin layer of semi-transparent calcite, part of the deposit has been eliminated thanks to progressive wearing with hard plastic brushes. In such a case, the wall has been greatly humidified and, through wearing, the calcite dust has flaked away. Thanks to this method, the veil grew thinner, came apart and the lines became clearer and partly visible through transparence. The technique allowed the discovery of the greater part of the reindeer frieze as well as the horses in the lateral diverticulum; these operations led to the discovery of outlines and representations hardly discernible or not discernible at all at the time when Henri BREUIL surveyed the cave.

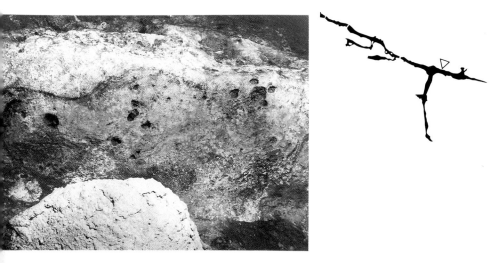

▲ After the intervention.

▼ Before the intervention.

Main gallery, left wall. First bison in the series of five.

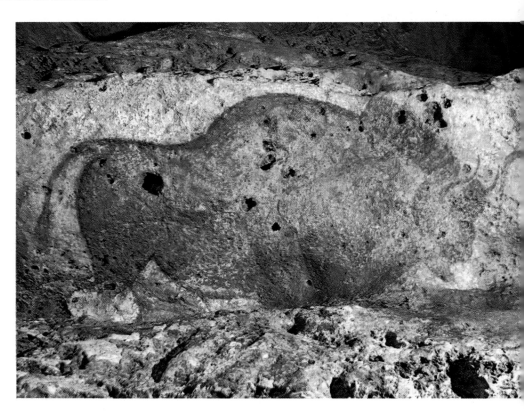

Washing and elimination of algae and mosses. The painted friezes were generally at the bottom of quite wet walls, the upper parts of which were covered with a thick clayey deposit; the percolation through the vault carried the clay on to the drawings. The phenomenon must have been intensified by the extra condensation caused by visitors. In fact, at Font-de-Gaume, the depositing of sediments was more pernicious than a trickling on the paintings themselves, even if it sometimes entailed a calcite deposit. Therefore all the clayey formations which lay upon the drawings or those tending to be carried on to them have been eliminated. It is always possible to fight the trickling on the decorated parts by fixing a drainage gutter above the threatened portions or rims of synthetic material; the latter having the advantage of provoking no irreversible consequences on the rock.

The washing of the walls has improved the general aspect of the cavity, thanks to the removing of the clayey parts and of the old smoky black due to the lighting by acetylene lamps. To grow, the algae need mineral salts, humidity, light and carbon dioxide; in cavities such as those of Font-de-Gaume and Lascaux, the almost permanent lighting, the strong ambient humidity, a small quantity of organic matter on the surface of the walls offer the required conditions of life. The vegetals, abundantly developing in the neighbourhood of the lighting points, have been eliminated by the spraying of a formal diluted solution.

Digging works. From the aesthetic point of view, setting off the discovered paintings presented a serious problem : their position at the bottom of the walls in the galleries, that is to say very near to the level of the ground : the drawings ran a risk since the visitors passed so close to them. The remedy was the lowering of the ground so that the decorated parts might be brought up to the level of the visitors'eyes. These operations have been realized after careful archeological sondages (1) under the supervision of officials from the Cultural Department.

The lighting. The lighting in the cave was reorganized during the works of 1973 and the equipment was devised in order to make the tourists' visit easier and at the same time to respect the strict conditions of preservation.

It is under a direct current voltage of 24 volts and operated by a series of electric switches placed at regular intervals all along the cave ; the latter disposition allows a limitation of the time each part is lighted. Two modes of lighting coexist : the first is a ground lighting which facilitates the visitors' progress ; the second lights the paintings ; to which must be added an emergency lighting system connected with a battery.

Thanks to a specialised equipment, the intensity of the lighting near the drawings has been checked.

---

(1) Directed by Professor PRAT from the University of Bordeaux I.

Excavating witness after lowering
the level of the ground.

Archeological sondages in the main
gallery in order to put the five
bison frieze out of reach of the
visitors.

The measures recorded in the decorated parts have revealed a lighting level quite below the tolerable threshold for things especially sensitive to light. Except for the lighting of the polychrome bison referred to, (which, since then, has been diminished), the general conditions of lighting are in keeping with the norms of protection of works of art. In this field, one must be very vigilant for the excess of light favours the implantation of algal colonies which, like all the photolithomorphic organisms find good conditions of development on a wet and well-lit base.

Maintenance. The alterations in the cavities and their surroundings since they were discovered, as well as the tourist frequentation are responsible for perturbations which must be regularly and carefully studied. The visitors' coming and going impede or increase the air currents; favouring the transportation of vegetal spores, of organic debris, which, as we have seen, may in turn permit the development of microorganisms. The spreading of such colonies on the decorated walls is detrimental to the sound preservation of the cave paintings and a regular maintenance must be ensured.

Within the « conservation des monuments historiques d'Aquitaine » (Aquitaine Historical Monuments Conservancy), a maintenance program has been devised and the cavity has been cleaned, biocidal solutions sprayed with satisfactory results : it is capital that this type of intervention should be carried out every year.

The studies and interventions described above have enabled us to master the influence of carbon dioxide and to restore the Font-de-Gaume cave to safe conditions of preservation of the cave paintings, even during the touristic season. In the cavity, and because of its relatively small size, any perturbation can have immediate consequences. Nevertheless, we are able to preserve a balance, however delicate, and it is advisable not to perturb it by modifying the basic conditions.

Font-de-Gaume is under scientific control and tests are regularly carried out to detect modifications, if any, which ensures the protection and conservation of the artistic inheritance it shelters : at the same time, it enables the general public to enjoy fully an infrequent contact with such an ancient and genuine piece of artistry.

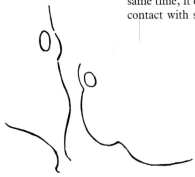

Contents

Made and printed by
Imprimerie Reymondie
for Editions Fanlac
près la tour de Vésone
Périgueux
20th February 1994

ISBN 2-86577-149-0